Milani and Friends
A Book for all young Princesses who will be Queens

5|8|00

Nylah you
are a
princess
who will
be a
Queen!

Jackie Jordan

by

Jackie Jordan, LMHC

Illustrated by: **Chauncey Alexander**

This book is dedicated to my granddaughter, Milani, and to all of the beautiful Princesses like her who will be Queens. I cannot forget my grandson, who, along with his twin sister Milani, give me so much joy and inspiration.

I'd like to acknowledge the many special people in my life, past and present, who have made me who I am today. Above all, I give thanks, praise and glory to my God, who has been with me and inspired me throughout this wonderful journey called life.

"There is nothing more beautiful than a flower in full bloom --- so it is with our girls when they blossom in their full potential."

Jackie Jordan

This Book Belongs To:

Name: _____

Please read with me!!

Milani
and
Friends

Hi, my name is Milani.

These are my friends.

We go to the same school and have been friends since the first grade. We are now in the third grade.

This is me and my twin brother, Devon, and these are my parents.

My father owns a barber shop downtown.

My mother works in a government office building.

This is my friend Patrice.

She lives with her mother who is a schoolteacher.

This is Kenya. She lives with her older brother and parents. Her parents own an African arts and crafts store downtown.

This is Reagan. She lives with her older sister and parents.

Her parents are both doctors and work at a hospital.

And this is LaShantae.

Her grandmother takes care of her, as well as her younger sister and brothers.

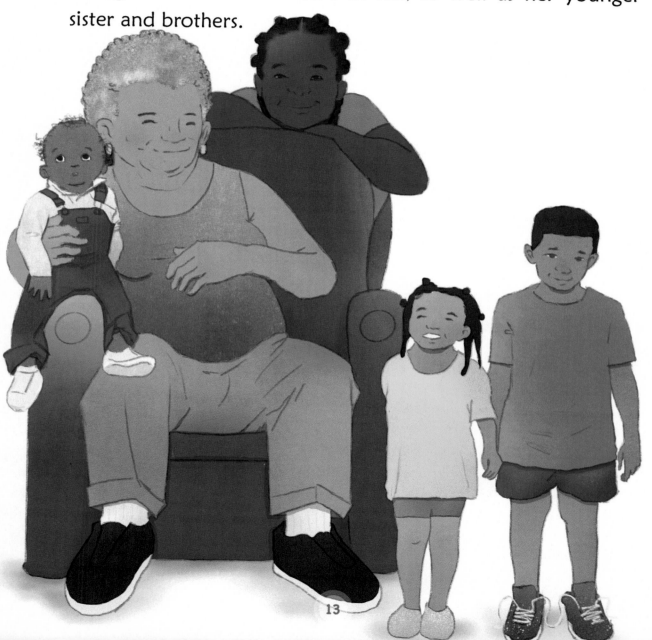

We all became good friends because a lot of kids at school picked on us. Kids made fun of me because of my gapped front teeth.

They picked on LaShantae and called her mean names because of her weight.

Kenya is really tall and skinny. Kids laughed at her and said her legs looked like sticks.

My friend, Patrice, is really, really smart and likes to read. They called her a nerd.

And they did not like Reagan because she lives in a great big house with a pool, and her parents are both successful doctors.

18

We felt very, very sad and left out. So, we started to sit together for lunch at school because no one else would sit with us.

But we soon learned that even though we are very different and unique, we are very, very special.

We have lots of fun together. We have sleepovers, we go to the park and to the playground. We also love to go to the movies and eat popcorn.

We don't worry about the other kids being mean to us because our parents and teachers are helping us learn that we are special, beautiful, fun, talented and smart. And that it is important to have good friendships.

We are learning how to like and appreciate ourselves.
Even though we each have our unique differences, we Really
Like Each Other!!

And now, some of those mean kids want to be our friends.

It is GOOD to have good friends!!!

Milani and Friends say:

Be kind to one another and treat others with respect.
Remember in order to have a friend, you must be a friend.
So, make a friend today!!

There is nothing more important than for children to grow up with a positive sense of self. It starts very young in life and must be strengthened and nurtured. Having positive friendships and nurturing children's positive strengths play an important part in strengthening their self-esteem. How can we help to accomplish this as parents, caregivers, and other important adults?

Here are some helpful tips.

1. Find out what are your child's positive strengths. What does she like? What is she good at doing? How is she talented, gifted, or special?

2. What are the things that other children can target or use negatively against her?

3. Help your child instill pride in her positive strengths and show her how to use them in a helpful and positive way.

4. For those areas that are not strong, help your child see that everyone has strengths but also weaknesses. Children, as well as adults, all have the potential to improve even in those areas where they are not strong.

5. Teach and encourage your child to find good, positive friends; friends that have something in common with them or friends that enjoy some of the same activities.

6. Understand that children, as well as adults, seek to be a part of a strong circle of supportive individuals whether it is only two or twenty people. Adults typically have the maturity to separate individuals in their world as either very close friends, casual associates, or impersonal acquaintances. However, young children see everyone as their "friend" and they sometimes find it hard and confusing when some of these "friends" are not kind to them. Parents and caregivers should have a conversation with their children to ask them, "Why is Johnny your friend?" or "What makes Mary your friend?"

7. Spend quality time with your child. "Meet" with her on a regular

basis to "check in" with her. Praise her for doing a good job or when she is engaged in positive activities. Give her more praise than punishment. Help build her self-esteem by telling her that she is "beautiful," "smart," "talented," "fun." Say it often so that she has it instilled in her mind and spirit.

8. When other children say mean and hurtful things to your children, remind them that they are special and that true "friends" do not say mean things to their friends.

9. Who are your children's "friends?" Find out, meet their parents, go out together as a group to activities. When the children see that their parents approve and are supportive of their friendship, they will feel more bonded with their "friends."

10. Talk to your children when they are faced with social challenges and tell them that you love them and care about their feelings. Ask them if there is anything that they would like for you to do to help them in the situation; or would they want to try to solve the problem on their own. Give them all the guidance and support that they need or ask for to address the problem.

Use this area to jot down your thoughts, ideas and information that you can use in one-on-one conversations with your child.

Notes:

_____

_____

_____

_____

_____

_____

_____

_____

_____

_____

_____

_____

_____

_____

_____

Notes:

_____

_____

_____

_____

_____

_____

_____

_____

_____

_____

_____

_____

_____

_____

_____

_____

_____

Notes:

_____

_____

_____

_____

_____

_____

_____

_____

_____

_____

_____

_____

_____

_____

_____

_____

_____

_____

Notes:

_____

_____

_____

_____

_____

_____

_____

_____

_____

_____

_____

_____

_____

_____

_____

_____

_____

_____

ABOUT THE AUTHOR

 **Jackie Jordan, MA, LMHC** is a licensed mental health counselor practicing in Orlando, Florida. She has worked as a mental health counselor/therapist for over twenty-five years in Maryland and Florida. She became licensed in the state of Florida in December of 2015.

Jackie has worked with children, adolescents, teens, adults, couples and families with different problems, issues, and challenges. Her passion is working with young girls in helping them to identify their positive strengths and talents to build their self-worth, self-esteem, and self-confidence. It has been a lifelong journey for Jackie, coming from a place of extreme lack of confidence and low-self-esteem, to finding out her true self and her true purpose. It has been her vision and mission to share these experiences with other young girls on their journeys to foster self-love, find respect from others and achieve greatness for the common good.

Made in the USA
Columbia, SC
21 March 2022

57908658R00022